■SCHOLASTIC
Phonics

Trent Gets a Pet

Published in the UK by Scholastic Education, 2022
Scholastic Distribution Centre, Bosworth Avenue, Tournament Fields, Warwick, CV34 6UQ
Scholastic Ireland, 89E Lagan Road, Dublin Industrial Estate, Glasnevin, Dublin, D11 HP5F

SCHOLASTIC and associated logos are trademarks and/or registered trademarks of Scholastic Inc.
www.scholastic.co.uk
© 2022 Scholastic Limited
1 2 3 4 5 6 7 8 9 2 3 4 5 6 7 8 9 0 1

Printed by Ashford Colour Press
The book is made of materials from well-managed, FSC-certified forests
and other controlled sources.

A CIP catalogue record for this book is available from the British Library.

ISBN 978-0702-30904-5

Every effort has been made to trace copyright holders for the works reproduced in this publication,
and the publishers apologise for any inadvertent omissions.

Author
Catherine Baker
Editorial team
Rachel Morgan, Vicki Yates, Abbie Rushton, Liz Evans
Design team
Dipa Mistry, Justin Hoffmann, Andrea Lewis, We Are Grace
Illustrations
Floss Pottage/Illo agency

Help your child to read!

This book practises words with more than one consonant next to each other, plus short vowel sounds (like '**cr**unch' or 'fe**lt**').
Read these words with your child:

flat   **bench**   **plan**   **slug**

Your child may need help to read these common tricky words:

he   **there**   **was**   **no**   **the**   **little**   **I**   **have**   **all**

Before reading

- Look at the cover picture and read the title together. Read the back cover blurb to your child.
- Ask your child: *What is Trent looking at in the cover picture? Do you think a slug would make a good pet? Why or why not?*

During reading

- If your child gets stuck on a word, remind them to sound it out and then blend the sounds to read the word: b-l-o-ss-o-m-s, blossoms.
- If they are still stuck, show them how to read the word.
- Enjoy looking at the pictures together. Pause to talk about the story.

After reading

- Ask your child: *Why couldn't Trent have a normal pet like a dog or cat?*
- *Would you like a slug as a pet? Why, or why not?*

Can you spot the chameleon on 6 pages?

Trent wished he had a pet.

But there was no room in his flat.

Trent sat on the bench.
He felt sad.

But then he spotted a little slug.

Trent picked blossoms and herbs for the slug.

crunch!
chomp!

The slug munched them all up.

Soon, the plot looked sad.

10

But now, the slug was big and strong. Trent felt glad!

The splendid slug munched turnips. It crunched pumpkins.

Soon, the slug was a star!

Trent got rich. He got a bigger flat, and a bigger garden.

But he kept his pet slug!

15

Retell the story

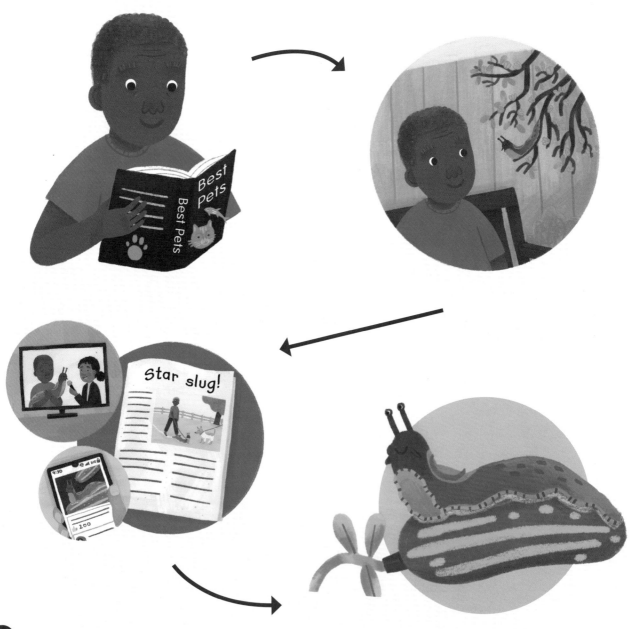